Alaska's
Mendenhall Glacier

photos by MARK KELLEY   written by NICK JANS

Publisher/Photographer: Mark Kelley
Author: Nick Jans
Designer: Matt Knutson
Digital Imaging Specialist: Terra Dawn Parker
Project Manager: Malou Peabody
U.S. Forest Service Advisors: John Neary, Nikki Hinds & Laurie Craig
History Consultant: Jim Geraghty
Proofreader: Leandra Lewis
Science Advisor: Dr. Matt Beedle

Printed in Canada by Friesens Corporation
A FSC® certified printer, a proud member
of the Green Press Initiative

Mark Kelley Photography
PO Box 32077, Juneau, AK 99803 / USA
Business Phone: (907) 586-1993
Toll Free: (888) 933-1993
FAX Number: (907) 586-1201
Email: photos@markkelley.com
Website: markkelley.com

Alaska's Mendenhall Glacier
ISBN 9781880865606 – Hardcover
ISBN 9781880865590 – Paperback
Third Printing 2023

Front Cover: Northern lights dance over the Mendenhall Glacier and reflect in open water near Steep Creek. Circa 2013

Page 1: Lupine line the pavement leading to the visitor center and frame the Mendenhall Glacier in the background. Circa 2018

Opposite Page: Kayakers paddle near the face of the Mendenhall Glacier. Circa 2014

Back Cover: The Mendenhall Glacier casts a mirror reflection in Mendenhall Lake. The best time for such conditions is usually early and late in the day, when terrain-driven winds are calmest. Circa 2004

Pages 4-5: Brotherhood Bridge Park's field of fireweed, peaking in mid to late July, provides a classic vista of the Mendenhall Glacier and surrounding peaks. Circa 2010

An Accessible Wonder

Across the gray-green sweep of Mendenhall Lake, a glacier of the same name rises: a great frozen river thirteen miles long, winding out of the massive Juneau Icefield. Cradled between jagged peaks, it grinds a sinuous path downhill, pulled by gravity and the weight of ice.

Over my years living in and traveling Alaska, I've seen thousands of glaciers, from tiny hanging relics high in the Brooks Range to thunderous tidewater beasts. While each one stands unique and gorgeous in its own way, I've never found a glacier that matches the postcard perfection of the Mendenhall. Whether viewed from afar or close up, this glacier glistens like a great, blue-white stone in a flawless setting: the soaring pinnacles of Stroller White Mountain and Mount

Campers soak up the morning view of the glacier from Thunder Mountain.
Circa 2014

Hikers pause at the junction of the West Glacier and Mount McGinnis trails. Circa 2016

McGinnis on the west; to the east, the precipitous ridge of Thunder Mountain merging into the massive pyramid of Bullard Mountain, punctuated by the gushing plume of Nugget Falls; and as a backdrop, the craggy spires of the Mendenhall Towers—all reflected in the lake, adrift with calved icebergs.

Though the glacier has altered considerably since famed naturalist John Muir viewed it in 1879, apparently little in its aesthetic appeal has changed. Muir named the Mendenhall Auk Glacier in honor of the local *Aak'w Kwaan* Tlingit clan, and declared it to be "one of the most beautiful of all the coastal glaciers."

When it comes to the Mendenhall, I confess my own bias. Drawn by

Visitors linger at aptly named Photo Point, just a short stroll from the visitor center. Circa 2008

its beauty and mystery, my wife Sherrie and I built a house two miles from the edge of its looming bulk, on ground where the glacier had stood just a lifetime before. For eight years, the glacier was our neighbor. We sometimes woke in the night to its thunder; watched seasons shift across its furrowed face; skied and paddled and clambered along its margins. Its cold radiance became a frame to our lives.

We weren't unique in our attachment. Thousands of Juneau residents look up from neighborhood streets, schools, the grocery store parking lot, or a weekend outing, and the Mendenhall rises above, implacable and timeless—so familiar, at times, that it's taken for granted; but when the glacier glows in a sudden burst of sun, or shimmers beneath northern lights, even the most jaded locals draw a collective breath, reminded of where they are.

What truly sets apart the Mendenhall from other Alaska glaciers is its incredible accessibility. From anywhere in Juneau, you can simply drive to the Forest Service's visitor center parking lot in a matter of minutes. No organized tour, specialized equipment, or athletic skills are necessary to stand a mile or less from the glacier's face, or hike miles of trails winding across nearby forest, beaches, and slopes. For the more ambitious, making much closer, even direct contact can be an afternoon trip rather than an expedition. In summer season, more than a half million visitors from around the world arrive to marvel at its splendor. The Mendenhall is truly Juneau's—and Alaska's—backyard glacier. Yet it remains a pristine wonder, an emblem of the Great Land's wild beauty, and a reminder of a vast, natural world that exists beyond our bidding. ❅

A group of local girls make the most of a summer afternoon in a small, sun-warmed pond on the east side of Mendenhall Lake. Circa 2005

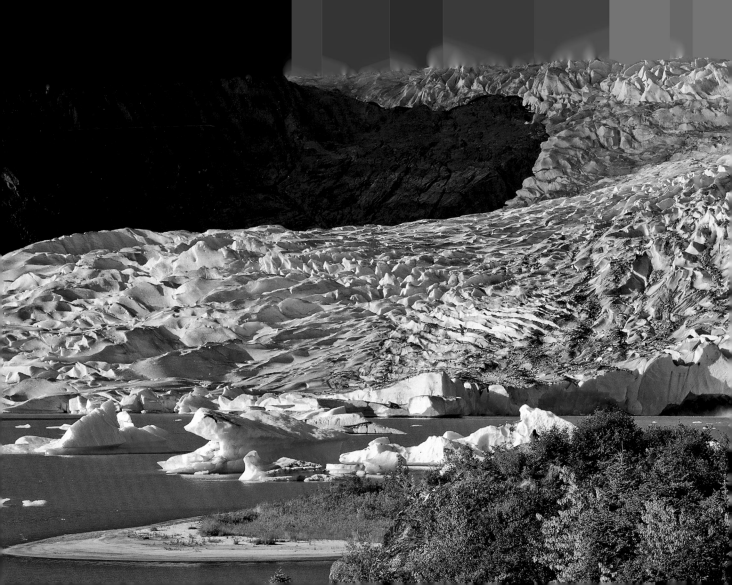

The Great Plow

Pioneering geologist Louis Agassiz called glaciers "God's great plow." While less dramatic than erupting volcanoes, earthquakes, or hurricanes, the power of glaciers to transform huge areas of the earth is stunning, at the edge of human comprehension. The results of that power are on full display in Southeast Alaska. The entire region was carved by an immense ice sheet that once sprawled across the region, so heavy the earth bowed and sagged beneath its weight.

Climate and topography make northern Southeast Alaska a perfect glacier factory. Pushed by prevailing winds, waves of warm, moisture-laden air swirl off the Pacific Ocean and slam into the Coast Range. As these masses of wet air are shoved inland and uphill, they cool rapidly and shed that moisture in sponge-wringing quantities. Along the coast and at lower elevations, that means rain most of the year, around 85 inches or more in downtown Juneau. This incredible precipitation nourishes a temperate rainforest teeming with life.

At higher elevations, heavy, wet snow falls instead of rain, a hundred-plus feet annually in some areas. Thanks to the region's cool, cloudy summers, it accumulates faster than it melts. Compressing under its own enormous weight, snow forms into ice—vast fields of it. Island peaks known as nunataks

With the glacier and a lake full of icebergs as a backdrop, a visitor enjoys a moment of solitude. Circa 2010

project above these frozen seas, offering limited but vital refuges for life. Ninety miles long, 45 wide, covering 1500 square miles and in places over 4,800 feet thick, the Juneau Icefield is the fifth largest such body in the western hemisphere, and one of the world's largest outside of Antarctica and Greenland. When you're standing downtown, or out by the Mendenhall Glacier Visitor Center, the Juneau Icefield looms unseen above, stretching south to the Taku River, and north to Skagway.

Perched on the shoulders of steep-sided mountains between four and nine thousand feet, those masses of ice have one place to go. Drawn by the force of gravity and propelled by its own weight, ice slides downhill, forming the flowing bodies we call glaciers. The downhill speed may range between inches and feet per day. Just like slow motion rivers, glaciers follow the path of least resistance; curve around obstacles; and gain momentum in steep spots. Unlike rivers, they carve distinctive, U-shaped valleys. The Juneau Icefield feeds 53 glaciers.

Due to its high-pressure formation and relative purity, glacier ice holds unique properties. It's harder and heavier than normal ice, yet surprisingly slick and flexible. Molding to the terrain and bearing down with immense force, it picks up and drags millions of tons of debris along—silt, sand, gravel, house-sized boulders, even entire forested hillsides if they happen to stand in the glacier's path. Much of this material is visible from above as dark bands called moraines. The rubble in turn scrapes against whatever it touches, greatly increasing the abrasive power of the ice. A glacier can grind the hardest bedrock. The lake's opaque cast is due to suspended silt called glacial flour: mountain ground to dust by the relentless power of ice.

But a glacier is far more than a destroyer; it's a transporter, builder, and transformer. It carves lakes and ponds; creates rivers and streams; and when the ice recedes, it leaves all that massive rock and soil behind, and a world tilled and ready for life to sprout anew. The Mendenhall Valley as we see it today was shaped by its glacier, and that process continues before our eyes, and will continue centuries from now. Change is the only constant. ❄

The view from the visitor center: Photo Point, the Mendenhall Glacier, Mendenhall Lake, and Nugget Falls. Circa 2018

The Dance of Life

As the glacier recedes, life takes hold on newly exposed rock. The process of succession begins. Lichens and mosses, bacteria, fungi, and wind-borne annual plants are among the first to arrive. Nitrogen-fixing lupine and alder soon follow, and are joined by willow and cottonwood. These hardy, pioneering species move through their life cycles and build up soil. Along the fringes of the melting glacier, trees and other organic matter from forests overrun hundreds, even thousands of years ago emerge from the ice, begin to decay, and provide more footholds for new life. Roots, as well as freeze-thaw cycles, expand cracks in rock surfaces, which in turn collect organic matter and become plant nurseries. Rain and cascading meltwater carve streambeds, fill lakes and kettle ponds.

Evergreen Sitka spruce and western hemlock take root in growing soil pockets, and begin their slow-but-steady pursuit of the faster-growing but shorter-lived broadleaf species. Insects, songbirds, small rodents,

Previous page: A kayaker paddles through whitecaps near the glacier's face. Sunlight refracting through the waterfall's mist creates the rainbow. Circa 2008

Canada geese fly in front of the Mendenhall Glacier and Mendenhall Towers. The Mendenhall Valley is a vital link in an important seasonal flyway for migratory birds. Circa 2000

Sockeye salmon display brilliant spawning colors. Also known as reds, they're the first of two salmon species to arrive in Steep Creek, by late July or early August. Coho or silvers show up roughly a month later and into freeze-up. Circa 2005

Bundled up in their thick winter coats, a mountain goat nanny and kid move to the lower elevations around Mendenhall Lake in winter, where less snowfall and more shelter make for easier foraging. Circa 2013

and more—myriad lives feast, find shelter, and raise young in a fast-greening world.

A multistoried, species-rich forest develops. Beavers and waterfowl make their homes in lush wetlands, and salmon are soon to follow. Higher up, mountain goats and marmots browse, and provide prey for wolves. Bears forage; eagles keen. Eventually, towering hemlock mix with spruce, forming a climax (old-growth) forest. The succession process takes more than three centuries. Once established, the old-growth forest might remain, essentially unchanged, for a thousand years or more. If the glacier were to advance, as it has before, it would sweep this green, vibrant world down to bare rock; and, when the glacier receded, the cycle would begin again. In the shadow of the glacier, the dance of life is dynamic—and beautiful as a wolf howl drifting on the wind. ❄

The photo on the left was taken in 1986, the one on the right in 2012. In these 26 years the Mendenhall Glacier retreated roughly a mile, and vertically thinned about 700 feet in places. Since 1750, the Mendenhall has withdrawn over three miles and the rate of ice loss has increased in recent decades.

The Melting River

Like all but a scant handful of Alaska's 10,000-plus glaciers, the Mendenhall is retreating at a breathtaking pace. When I first visited the Mendenhall in the early 1990s, it lay more than a half mile closer to the visitor center; Nugget Falls, that dramatic, white-gushing cascade on the eastern crease of Bullard Mountain, was just emerging from behind a wall of ice. The brushy rock outcropping that stretches across the northwest corner of the lake was still overlain by tongues of ice. But the Mendenhall's greater length in those not-so-long-ago days wasn't nearly as impressive as its total mass. The main body of the glacier, winding uphill into the Juneau Icefield, stood nearly 700 feet taller in places than it does today. Over just a quarter century, hundreds of millions of tons of ice have vanished.

The reason is simple. The Mendenhall is losing ice much faster at lower elevations than it is gaining at higher elevations. Think of a valley glacier as a slow-motion, frozen river. The speed and volume of its flow is determined by snow accumulation at its headwaters. If the source—in the Mendenhall's case, the Juneau Icefield—isn't receiving enough snow to compress into ice and sustain its gravity-driven flow, the river dwindles. If snowfall were to exceed the loss rate for several decades, the Mendenhall would advance, as it has in the past.

One can't exactly call the Mendenhall's current condition a drought. While sunny, warm days contribute to ice loss (ablation) through melting,

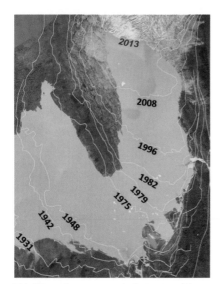

This illustration maps out the ice retreat of the Mendenhall Glacier since 1931.

convection, and calving, rain likewise hastens the melting process—and Southeast Alaska is, after all, a rainforest, with many areas annually receiving those 100-plus inches of precipitation at sea level, and up to a 100 feet of snow on the Juneau Icefield. One might think that totals more than enough to sustain the Mendenhall and its dozens of sister glaciers; but the frequency of above-freezing days, whether rainy or sunny, both at elevation and near the glacier's lower reaches, is much higher than in centuries past. The difference between solid and liquid water is just a single degree. The former nourishes a glacier; the latter melts it.

If the Mendenhall Glacier of today seems a shadow of its former self just two decades ago, consider the view into geologic time. Waves of glaciation have ebbed and flowed across this landscape over the past 1.5 million years. The tide-swept fiords of the Inside Passage that today are plied by cruise ships were once the valleys of enormous tidewater glaciers carving their way to sea level—one that lay worldwide 400 feet lower, due to so much of the planet's water being held as ice. Comparatively minor (but still massive) advances and retreats aside, we emerged from that most recent glacial maximum roughly 10,000 years ago.

The Mendenhall as we recognize it today is at least 3,000 years old. Its most recent advance occurred during the "Little Ice Age" that gripped the world from the 15th into the mid-18th century. The Mendenhall left a marker of that advance, circa 1750, near the current location of Taku Boulevard: a terminal moraine of rocky rubble stretching across the valley, over three miles from the glacier's current face.

Huge astrophysical and planetary forces, including cyclic variations in the earth's orbit around the sun and wobbles in its rotation, are likely triggers for major climate shifts. However, little doubt remains among mainstream climate scientists that human activity over the past century is fueling our current rapid warming trend. They point to ancient ice and sediment cores that demonstrate that this current global warming event is the fastest ever recorded, when in fact we should be in a natural cooling cycle. What's more, there are no known factors except our own production of greenhouse gases that can explain the pace. Computer models, which have become increasingly sophisticated and data-supported, also point to human activity as a major contributor to our warming climate. When I ask glaciologist Dr. Matt Beedle of the Juneau Icefield Research Program (JIRP) how sure he is of the human factor, he says without hesitation, "as confident as I can be."

The short-term future of the Mendenhall Glacier seems bleak. Beedle, himself a born-and-raised Juneauite, offers an educated guess that the glacier he's known his entire life will no longer touch the lake within 5-10 years. A major paper published in 2016 by a team of respected glaciologists calculates that at current rates of ice loss, the great Juneau Icefield itself, along with the glaciers it nour-

ishes, may vanish in fewer than two centuries.

However, the same paper offers an alternate scenario. If greenhouse gases decrease and the warming rate slows as expected due to regulation and utilization of alternate energy

sources, the icefield may stabilize after losing more than half its mass. In other words, the future of the mighty Mendenhall, and thousands of other glaciers worldwide, which together with the ice sheets contain 70 percent of the planet's fresh water, could well lie in our hands. ❄

The Gilkey Trench on the Gilkey Glacier of the Juneau Icefield features distinct dark stripes, known as moraines—bands of rock and soil the glacier has gouged from the valley as it grinds downhill. There are two types of moving moraines. Lateral moraines run down the edges of a flowing glacier, and it's obvious that the material comes from adjacent slopes. Medial moraines (away from the edges) are the result of two valleys of glacial ice meeting, and one lateral moraine being pushed toward the middle. You can count the number of tributaries a glacier has by counting its medial moraines. Circa 2016

Blue Ice

Glacier blue ice is a sight to behold and certainly a wonderful reason to visit the Mendenhall Glacier Recreation Area.

Glacier blue ice is very dense. Fresh snowfall on a glacier contains about 80% air. After a year or so and under pressure from new snow above, the delicate snowflakes turn into tiny pellets called firn, which contains about 50% air. In Southeast Alaska, it does not take very long, maybe 4-6 years, for firn to turn into glacier ice with less than 20% air remaining between crystals. Over time and under increasing pressure, even more air will escape, making glacier ice heavy and dense. As light strikes this dense ice, the crystalline structure absorbs all colors of the light spectrum except blue. Glacier ice crystals refract blue light, and that is what our eye can see.

When ice calves off a glacier, the newly exposed ice appears exceptionally blue. The crystalline ice structure responsible for the blue color remains intact for only a few days. In time, air and surface melt breaks down the ice, causing it to fade to white – a color that denotes many tiny air bubbles in the ice. ❄

The glacier casts a mirrored image into Mendenhall Lake, just before freeze-up. Glaciers almost always looks the bluest in late fall and early winter, when dwindling rain and solar exposure results in slower weathering of ice. Circa 2012

Journey Into Time

I lean forward, scanning the enormity of the Mendenhall Glacier as our helicopter swoops low, hovers, and settles near the foot of the great, crevasse-riddled icefall— so named because it's a point where the glacier's smooth surface fractures into deep crevasses as it plunges downhill like a waterfall. Though I'd lived in the shadow of the glacier for years, I'm as awestruck as any of my fellow passengers. The helicopter might as well have been a time machine, carrying us not only up, but back thousands of years into a world ruled by ice.

We step out into that hauntingly gorgeous country, high on the glacier's shoulder. Donning crampons and climbing harnesses, we wander in a broad arc—first near a slope, where

Helicopter visitors examine a melt pond on the glacier. The glacier has many such clear blue melt ponds and streams coursing their way across the ice surface. Circa 2005

Rafting tourists float down the fireweed-lined Mendenhall River. Circa 2011

people. Most of them are thrilled to view the glacier from the visitor center and area trails, which range from wheelchair accessible to challenging. Thanks to the magic carpet provided by helicopters, tens of thousands of visitors each year, of all abilities, are able to not just view this grand ice palace from the ground, but to fly over, and even make direct contact with it.

A flight to the glacier is nothing short of exhilarating. Less than a minute after liftoff, passengers find themselves skimming weightlessly over ridges, the dazzling panorama of the Juneau Icefield stretching ahead. The going is every bit as spectacular as the destination. Dogsled rides, ice climbing, cave explorations, guided or independent walkabouts or paddling trips, and scenic flyovers—each choice is less an excursion than a transformative journey. ❄

we practice climbing skills; then we follow clear ice water rivulets downhill, to the edge of a blue moulin draining into the glacier's heart. It's almost impossible to imagine the depth of ice beneath my feet: as much as 1000 feet—and perhaps double that at the upper edge of the icefall.

Thanks to the Mendenhall's drive-up accessibility, it's visited each year by more than a half million

A group of guided glacier trekkers on the Juneau Icefield skirt a surface melt pond at the terminus of the Gilkey Glacier, with Horn Spire in the background. Circa 2011

The Heart of Ice

"There's the opening," Mark Kelley points. We scramble down an icy slope, toward the muffled rush of water. Before us, a portal to another world beckons: an ice cave leading under the Mendenhall Glacier's western edge. We pause to don rain gear, cinch up rubber knee boots and check camera settings.

Though every glacier seems solid ice, there's always water—a seasonally fluctuating rush of melt and rain streaming down its face and margins, diving into crevasses, and working its way toward bedrock. Even in winter, water finds its way through most glaciers. These flowages, ranging

A hiker visits one of the several ice caves
along the edge of the Mendenhall Glacier.
Circa 2009

A hiker gets a cold drink inside an ice cave. In summer, melting temperatures create continious rain from the icy ceiling. Circa 2014

from trickles to torrents, hasten the melting process; lubricate the glacier's downhill flow; and gnaw a shifting labyrinth of passages through its core. Vertical, water-carved entrance points on the glacier's surface are known as moulins. As water obeys the relentless call of gravity, it carves caverns into the ice. And when water levels recede, some of these caves become accessible.

While this particular cave is fairly stable, and doesn't require technical skills or equipment, our trip is far from a casual stroll. The approach hike includes some steep uphill going, then a mile of rough-trail scrambling over roots, boulders, and loose scree. Falling ice and rock pose constant hazards, especially around the cave entrance. Inside conditions

A winter ice cave explorer gazes up through a moulin, a nearly vertical, circular shaft created by downward-boring water. Water cascading down another moulin in the left side of this image froze into a column. Circa 2014

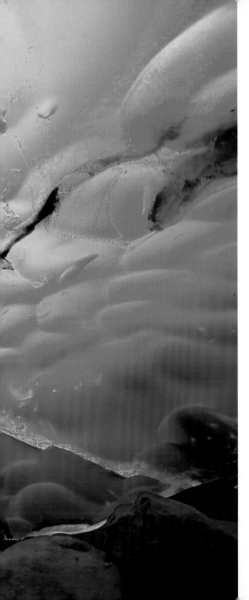

demand at least full coverage rain gear and boots, local knowledge, and surefooted agility.

Mark and I duck out of the bright summer day into the ten-foot-wide opening. Within a few yards, we're wading a boulder-studded stream, then clambering down a waterfall. The sloping, roughly oval-shaped chamber we enter might as well be an undersea grotto on some far planet. The mist-laden air itself is suffused with a liquid, luminescent blue glow, and a deep rumble seems to rise from everywhere. If Mark and I stand more than a few feet apart, we have to shout to each other.

Steady trails of water drip and drizzle from the ceiling and join the roiling stream. Within a few dozen yards, the cave tapers. At its far end, water plunges into a narrowing passage that leads the steep last quarter mile to Mendenhall Lake.

Mark and I stand, bathed in the strange blue light, framing images, hoping to capture the essence of this surreal place, carved into the heart of ice. Water drips off our rain gear. The chill, moist air fills our lungs; light filtering from the entrance casts strange patterns on the gleaming walls. Over our heads, thousands of tons of ice loom. There's a seductive sense of timelessness here, a whispered invitation to linger. But the circular warm glow of our own world, filtering through from above, beckons. And we go. ❄

Ice pillows inside an ice cave create an
other-worldly effect. Circa 2009

Local Time

Summer gives way to autumn. As the crowds by the visitor center dwindle, cottonwoods and willows glow, their colors shimmering in the lake. Bright, sun-warmed days alternate with brooding mist and rain; the cries of geese and cranes echo down the sky. Spawning salmon swirl in the creeks, and the bears shift into overdrive, foraging almost nonstop. Days shorten. As cold rains pelt from a lowering sky, leaves fade and fall. The land settles inward; its breathing slows. Snow dusts the mountains, then vanishes—but as the season progresses, the snowline creeps ever downward. High on the icefield, the first big snows have already fallen. The lake freezes around its margins; slush ice whispers down the river, clumps in eddies. One clear morning, the lake is sheeted with ice, and the wind falls hard from the north. The dark, cold dream of winter descends.

Cottonwoods ablaze with autumn colors on the shore of Mendenhall Lake. Circa 2008

Three hikers stroll through fresh snow on the frozen surface of Mendenhall Lake. Circa 2013

Winter is the heart and soul of the glacier, a time of renewal. How much snow falls and sticks, and the total number of hours below freezing over days, centuries, and millennia will determine the glacier's future. Though the overall warming trend is well documented, each year's winter is unique. Over the span of my years living by the glacier, I can recall winters when the ground was nearly bare for months and rains swept over us in endless sheets; others when we felt half smothered in snow, and the last drifts clung into early June. Cold snaps down to 20 below zero balanced against eerily sudden, warm chinook winds when temperatures soared into the 50s.

Though ice and cold make life harder—snow to shovel or plow, higher heating bills, more clothing,

The Aurora Borealis forms an arch over the Mendenhall Glacier. Circa 2017

A figure skater glides on glass-smooth ice past the glacier's reflection. Circa 2009

At sunset in December, a lone skater crosses Mendenhall Lake, headed toward Skater's Cabin, nearly three miles from the glacier's face. Circa 1998

slower travel—little doubt that most Juneauites hope for the sort of winters the old timers recall. They, like the glacier, are nourished by snow; it's why they're here. A few good storms, and the 6000 acre Mendenhall Glacier Recreation Area becomes Juneau's winter playground.

Dozens of miles of trails are served by a variety of access points, some of them well marked, others neighborhood secrets. Regardless of weather or time of day, there are always a few diehards out there—hiking, skiing, snowshoeing, snapping pictures, sledding with the kids, snowmobiling in

The flow of Steep Creek creates an open pond, reflecting the mountains around the glacier. Circa 2014

A sledder flies down a small but steep hill created by a sediment-covered iceberg called a "kame," which created one of Juneau's most popular mini-playgrounds. Located along the lake shore near Steep Creek's mouth, and referred to as "the sledding hill" by locals, it has been slowly shrinking as the underlying ice has melted. Circa 1998

permitted areas, exploring ice caves, or just taking a lunchtime walk with a world-class backdrop. Dogs are almost as numerous as people, and it's arguable who's having more fun. Local volunteers set and maintain miles of cross-country ski trails; spirited hockey games are staged on the ice by aptly named Skater's Cabin, a stone warm-up shelter dating back to the 1930s. A scattered few engage in extreme sports, including technical ice climbing, parasailing, or back-country snowboarding. On perfect days, snow-dusted or sun-bright, the glacier area absorbs hundreds of people, nearly all of them Juneau residents. But due to the expanse and the variety of possibilities, it seldom seems crowded. No doubt about it—winter at the Mendenhall is local time. They've earned it. ❄

Juneau residents wander the frozen lake, among a garden of icebergs. Circa 2005

SUMMER

This blue heron looks like it might be stalking the swamps of the deep south, but in fact is standing in Steep Creek, less than two miles from the Mendenhall Glacier. Circa 2009

WINTER

The great blue heron is one of the few large birds that can survive winter near the glacier. Herons often hunt young salmon in the open, flowing water of Steep Creek. Circa 2016

SUMMER

With the Mendenhall Glacier in the background, an exuberant but chilly young man dashes through the icy water in front of Nugget Creek Falls. Circa 2011

WINTER

An ice climber scales the frozen face of Nugget Creek Falls. Circa 2010

The Ice Lab

Scattered across the 1500 square miles of the Juneau Icefield lie clusters of small, weather-beaten buildings. Accessible only by air or on foot, at altitudes approaching a mile above sea level, they're unoccupied and encased in snow for most of the year. However, in the brief summer season, these field stations of the Juneau Icefield Research Program (JIRP) buzz with activity: dozens of scientists and students from around the world.

Initiated by Dr. Maynard Miller, in cooperation with William O. Field in 1948, JIRP has grown over the succeeding decades to become a globally recognized institution for glacier research

Perched at the top of the Gilkey Glacier, Camp 18 is one of the roughly two dozen outposts for the Juneau Icefield Research Program, spread across the Juneau Icefield. Circa 2016

and student enrichment. JIRP has worked collaboratively with, or been supported by numerous organizations, agencies, and universities, including The American Geographical Society and The Foundation for Glacier and Environmental Research. The University of Alaska Southeast also collaborates with JIRP, and conducts its own impressive research program.

As a result, the Juneau Icefield and its associated glaciers have become among the most studied on the planet, a gigantic outdoor laboratory for exploring a broad variety of cross-disciplinary subjects and issues, including, of course, glacial retreat and climate change, and the planet-wide challenges they pose. Hundreds of scientific papers, studies, and articles have been published as a result of JIRP and University of Alaska affiliated projects.

Cross-country skiers glide past Split Thumb on the Juneau Icefield. Circa 1999

A floatplane cruises over the roughly 1,500 square mile Juneau Icefield, larger than the state of Rhode Island. Circa 1997

JIRP not only initiates and facilitates research, but features a two-month program for students, who learn icefield skills, assist in research, and gain knowledge through hands-on field experience. Many are influenced in their career choices by this sojourn. In the words of Dr. Benjamin Santer, member of the JIRP faculty and the U.S. National Academy of Sciences, the Icefield "is the best—and grandest—Earth Sciences classroom in the world." JIRP director of academics and research Dr. Matt Beedle (who fell in love with glacier science as a high schooler through his JIRP experience) adds, "Through our students, we see this landscape with a new set of eyes." ❄

Jökulhlaup!

In 2011, the Mendenhall Valley was swept by a dynamic phenomenon. In late spring, pilots noted rising water in Suicide Basin, a small valley on the southeastern edge of the glacier, behind Mount Bullard. Scientists monitored the event as warming days and rain ate at the winter's snowpack, and runoff cascaded down Bullard's flank. Instead of draining into Mendenhall Lake, water continued to well in the basin, trapped by a wall of glacial ice. As meltwater poured down, a deepening lake formed—millions of gallons putting ever more pressure on an ice dam within Mendenhall Glacier. In early June, the dam ruptured, sending an icy flash flood under the glacier and into Mendenhall Lake: a phenomenon known to glaciologists as a *jökulhlaup* (in the Icelandic language, literally "glacier run"). Fed by this massive outflow, the lake rose two feet a day for a week, flooding beaches, trails, and low-lying forest. The swift, shallow Mendenhall River, the lake's only outlet, rose with breathtaking suddenness, spilling over its banks. Soil, brush, and trees were scoured away; the murky torrent roiled against the foundations of riverside houses as residents scrambled to rescue property and erect makeshift flood barriers.

Just when it seemed that the damage might be calamitous, the waters began to subside. Within several days, the river returned to high normal flow. The *jökulhlaup* had passed.

That was the first such modern-day event recorded at the Mendenhall, but not the last. *Jökulhlaups* have since repeated annually during the melt season—in some years, several times. Some are so slight they blend into normal melt or rain-related fluctuations and pass with little notice; others have been obvious. None has yet reached catastrophic proportions, but the possibility looms. The glacier keeps its secrets well. ❄

Photo Point Trail bench at low water in autumn. Circa 2016

Photo Point Trail during a Jökulhlaup flood. Circa 2015

The Bears of Steep Creek

On a late August day, dozens of visitors stand transfixed on the boardwalk bridge spanning Steep Creek, just yards from the visitor center parking lot. Just below them, a female black bear snatches a red sockeye salmon from the clear water and hauls it up the bank to her two cubs. The family feasts; then the cubs nurse and nap, oblivious to the whir of cameras and murmured voices. It's just another day for the bears, but an unforgettable moment for the watchers.

Over the past two decades, a modest but steady number of black bears, featuring several well-studied females with accompanying cubs, have become conditioned to human presence near the Mendenhall Glacier. Due to careful crowd management, a strict no-food rule for visitors, and enforced out-of-bounds areas separating people and bruins, these bears have come to see us as neither threat nor food source, yet remained wild: a state known as neutral habituation, the gold standard for wildlife

A black bear leads her first-year cubs along Steep Creek, looking for salmon. Circa 2007

viewing management. In fact, these resident bears seem to use humans as a safety shield that deflects large, less people-tolerant males from their cubs.

One particular female with a distinctive notched ear has raised an astounding total of thirteen cubs along Steep Creek between 2003 and 2016, including two singles, four sets of twins and one litter of triplets. This tolerance of humans seems to be a learned behavior, passed on from mother to offspring, and possibly genetically selected as well. These bears are a truly unique and valuable resource, providing safe and sometimes spectacular walk-up viewing for thousands of lucky visitors each year.

Framed by 4,200 foot Mt. McGinnis and a lake filled with icebergs, a lone bear walks up Steep Creek. Circa 2007

"This place continues to amaze me with the opportunities people have for world class experiences," says longtime Forest Service naturalist Laurie Craig. "It is an immense privilege to tell the stories of wild black bears through those that we know here."

After waking from their nearby winter dens, the Steep Creek bears forage on newly emerged growth in May and June, often within sight of the visitor center. Cottonwoods in the area show the scars of high-climbing, branch-breaking bears seeking sweet new buds. As the snow line recedes, many bears work uphill, following the most succulent and nutrient-rich vegetation. In summer they begin to focus on berries, and

A black bear strolls along the Mendenhall Lake beach near the outlet of Steep Creek. Circa 2010

A large black bear snatches a bright red sockeye salmon, just a few yards from the viewing platform at the lower meadows of Steep Creek. Circa 2007

into autumn, feast on those, plus salmon moving into Steep Creek and other area streams—staggered, overlapping runs featuring sockeye (red) and coho (silver) salmon. Some nearby streams harbor chum and pink salmon as well. As the salmon runs fade, the bears turn to starchy roots, tubers, and late berries before denning up for the winter. It's a cycle that repeats, year after year, with natural variations.

Despite their relative abundance, you can't count on seeing a bear (or a porcupine, vole, or beaver, for that matter) over an hour or two on any

Sibling cubs wade the creek's shallows. Black bears display wide color variations, ranging from black, through shades of brown, to nearly white. Circa 2007

given day. But be assured they're there, often within a few yards. Seeing—not only animals and birds, but the natural world itself—requires us to slow down, lean in, and pay attention. Rustling brush, scents drifting on the wind, trampled grass, claw marks, and scat: even if we don't glimpse a single bear, the signs of their presence surround us. Savor the entire experience, including the mystery of the unseen. ❋

Left: Visitors crowd the viewing platform, straining to capture images of the bears along Steep Creek. Circa 2007
Above: After enjoying a salmon meal, a contented black bear leans back against a small willow scratching her chest and licking the last delicious morsel from her paws. Circa 2007

The Glacier Wolf

The Glacier Wolf. Circa 2007

The Mendenhall Glacier Recreation Area hosts a rich variety of wildlife, from mountain goats to beavers. Wolves have long been part of the ecological mix, but true to their elusive nature, tracks, scats, and an occasional howl are often the only evidence of their passing. However, in late autumn of 2003, hikers with dogs began encountering a lone black wolf—a young, black male—on a regular basis. Not only was he oddly tolerant of humans, he engaged dogs in a sociable, playful manner. The wolf, known to some as "Romeo," and to others simply as "the black wolf" or "the glacier wolf," came and went over six years. He was most frequently sighted during the winter months, when Mendenhall Lake and surrounding wetlands were frozen. Though he was habituated to human presence and socially bonded to dogs, he remained a free-ranging and highly successful wild predator, and sometimes disappeared for weeks or months at a time. In 2009, he was killed by poachers, who were apprehended. A bronze plaque on the trail to Nugget Falls commemorates his story, and Juneau's affection for this remarkable animal. In addition, an interpretive exhibit in the visitor center featuring him reclining on a rock, as well as his paw print and recorded howls, was completed in early 2017. ❄

On winter patrol, the black wolf known as "Romeo" crosses Mendenhall Lake. Circa 2007

On the Move

By their very nature, glaciers invite us to ponder the sweep of time, and gradual, eons-long processes. But in fact, Southeast Alaska ranks among the most dynamic and rapidly transforming landscapes on the planet. Twenty thousand years ago (a heartbeat by geologic standards), a great ice sheet lay draped across nearly all of Southeast Alaska as the Wisconsin Ice Age peaked. A glacier 3,000 feet deep swallowed what we now call the Mendenhall Valley; only the tips of Mount McGinnis, Bullard, and higher peaks were visible as jagged nunataks where life clung.

Just ten thousand years later, all that seemingly permanent ice had been swept away, and the valley transformed. A worldwide warming had led to a massive rise in sea level, and the valley was flooded to a depth of 400 feet. The water gradually receded as the valley floor, freed of that huge burden of ice, rebounded and rose. By 3,000 years before the present, we would have been able to recognize the basic shape of the Mendenhall Valley as we know it today: the glacier at its head, drained by streams feeding a glacial river cutting through a forested lowland, and the familiar forms of the surrounding mountains.

But the grinding power of ice would return. Roughly 800 years ago, a cooling trend known as The Little Ice Age led to a glacial advance that by 1770 brought the Mendenhall roughly three miles forward of its 2016 position. Since that advance, the Mendenhall's been in its current retreat. The Mendenhall's story can be read in great hillside striations, fossils, masses of glacial rubble, and vegetation lines.

Whatever snapshot you take of the Mendenhall Glacier on a given day is just that: a momentary image of a landscape in constant motion. ❄

This is the oldest known photo of the Mendenhall Glacier, taken in 1894 by William Ogilvie, showing Stoller White Mountain, Mendenhall Towers and Bullard Mountain. Jim Geraghty Collection.

Mendenhall Lake and Glacier, Alaska

Of Ice and Men—A Mendenhall Timeline

AUK VILLAGE

Auk Village, Circa 1888

SECRETARY SEWARD   EDWARD STOECKEL,   CHARLES SUMNER
Russian Minister
SIGNING THE TREATY FOR THE PURCHASE OF ALASKA
From the painting by Emanuel Leutze   By courtesy of the owner, William H. Seward, Jr.

1600 AD or earlier

Aak'w Kwaan Tlingit establish a village on the beach at the current site of Auke Bay Recreation Area. They call the glacier *Aak'wtaaksit*, "the glacier behind the little lake" (referring to Auke Lake, not Mendenhall Lake, which did not yet exist).

1700s-early 1800s

The Russians and Europeans (French, Spanish, and English) explore Southeast Alaska and give names to geographic features, many of which remain on modern maps.

1867

Secretary of State William Seward closes deal for U.S. purchase of Alaska from Russia for $7.2 million, and most Americans consider it a grand waste of money. Newspapers mock the purchase as "Seward's Folly" and "Seward's Ice Box."

A Trevor Davis photo taken from Skater's Cabin.
Jim Geraghty Collection. Circa 1940

Juneau, Circa 1887

Mendenhall Glacier, Circa 1930s

Covered Bridge Over Mendenhall River, Circa 1940s

Nugget Creek Power House, Circa 1920

1880s

Gold miners arrive from lower 48 and establish settlement at the site of present-day downtown Juneau. In 1880, local Tlingit chief Kawa.ee leads prospectors Joe Juneau and Richard Harris up what's now known as Gold Creek to Silverbow Basin and a modest-sized gold rush is off and running. The town was originally named Harrisburg, then changed to Rockwell. In 1881, miners voted to change the name to Juneau.

1879–1891

The glacier is renamed Auk Glacier by famed naturalist John Muir to honor the local Tlingit clan. In 1891 it's officially renamed Mendenhall for Thomas Corwin Mendenhall, superintendent of the U.S. Coast and Geodetic Survey that was charged with mapping the boundary between Alaska and Canada.

1903

Men in horse-drawn wagon cross the first bridge to span the Mendenhall River.

1912-1914

Local mining giant Treadwell Mines builds Nugget Creek powerhouse and tramway, creating 2.3 megawatts of hydropower to run their mill on Douglas Island, and sell surplus power to citizens as well. In December 1943, the powerhouse, rendered obsolete by the Salmon Creek dam, is boarded up and closed. Neglected and in disrepair, it's finally torn down and removed by the U.S. Forest Service in 1965.

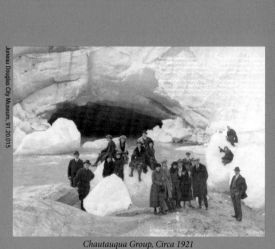

Chautauqua Group, Circa 1921

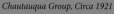

President Harding and Party, Circa 1923

Skater's Cabin, Circa 1939

Biplane Over Auke Lake and Mendenhall Glacier, Circa 1926

1921

An early band of tourists poses at the glacier. Dating back to the turn of the 20th century, the Mendenhall's unique combination of exotic beauty and relative accessibility attracts visitors from near and far. The people in this image are part of a Chautauqua group. The Chautauqua was a national movement of artists presenting a stimulating series of lectures, musical performances, readings, and plays.

1923

Warren G. Harding becomes the first president of the United States to visit Alaska. Traveling to the territory by ship and rail, he visited the Mendenhall Glacier on July 10, 1923 as part of an extended stay to celebrate the completion of the Alaska Railroad. He dies in San Francisco on his return trip home.

1926

An aerial survey team is dispatched from the U.S. Naval Air Station in San Diego with a crew of 114 and three biplanes to photograph the Tongass National Forest. The multi-year shoot results in tens of thousands of images, all taken from an altitude of 10,000 feet.

1936

Men of the Admiralty Division of the Civilian Conservation Corps (CCC) construct a stone-walled shelter on the west shore of Mendenhall Lake, known as Skater's Cabin. Popular with residents and visitors, it suffers a devastating roof fire in 1988 but is restored by local volunteers. Skater's Cabin is now on the National Register of Historic Places.

The Sign-in Station, a Precursor to Visitor Center, Circa 1960

Lassie at Governor's Mansion in Juneau, Episode #480 "The Last Frontier," features the Mendenhall Glacier. Circa 1968

Juneau Icefield Research Program Camp #17, Circa 2016

1947

Regional Forester Frank Heintzleman announces that the glacier and surrounding lands, known as the Mendenhall Lake Recreation Area, are "reserved for public recreation and closed to all occupancy and use inconsistent with recreation use." This 6,000 acre preserve is later renamed the Mendenhall Glacier Recreation Area.

Bus Parking Lot, Circa 1950

1948

The Juneau Icefield Research Program (JIRP) is initiated. Dr. Maynard Miller leads a small group of explorers on a reconnaissance trip that launches one of the world's longest continuous studies monitoring ice and climate change in a single location.

1960-81

The Mendenhall Glacier and Juneau Icefield get Hollywood exposure, including the 1960 film starring Richard Burton, The Ice Palace; an episode of the TV series Lassie; and John Carpenter's 1981 remake of the sci-fi classic, The Thing. One of the JIRP research stations has a cameo in the latter.

A Treeless Visitor Center from Photo Point Trail, Circa 1962

U.S. Forest Service Collection

Inside the Visitor Center, Circa 1962

U.S. Forest Service Collection

Photo by Mark Kelley

The Remodeled Visitor Center Surrounded by Trees, Circa 2006

1962

The original Mendenhall Glacier Visitor Center is dedicated. Designed by local architect Linn Forrest, it's the Forest Service's first ever such facility, anywhere. From 1968 to 1973 it includes a coffee shop owned by Joe and Kitty Stehlik, whose homemade pies are made famous by radio newscaster Lowell Thomas on his 1970 trip to Alaska. Local KJ Metcalf, the center's first naturalist, helps start the ever-popular Fireside Chat series, the longest-running program of its type in any national forest facility. The original visitor center was designed to accommodate roughly 28,000 visitors per year, and by the time a remodel is begun in 1997, annual visitation is close to 300,000. The renovation is completed in 1999.

1975

First recorded death at the glacier. Falling ice kills a Seattle woman standing too close to the glacier's face near Nugget Falls. Several other accidental deaths have been recorded since in the 6,000-acre recreation area due to falls and avalanches. Most are locals engaged in off-trail activities.

1980

Alaska Travel Adventures pioneers commercial raft trips down the Mendenhall River.

Photo by Mark Kelley

Raft on Mendenhall Glacier, Circa 1990

TEMSCO Helicopter Over Mendenhall Glacier,
Circa 1995

Black Wolf "Romeo" with Local Dog "Dakota," Circa 2003

Mendenhall Glacier Ice Caves, Circa 2017

1983

The first Helicopter Glacier Tour lands on the glacier and the Juneau Icefield, pioneered by TEMSCO Helicopters.

1997

ERA Helicopters introduces dog mushing tours. TEMSCO and Coastal Helicopters follow suit. NorthStar Trekking develops the Helicopter Glacier Trek.

2003-2009

"Romeo," the Mendenhall's sociable black wolf, plays with dogs and becomes a popular, well-known fixture until his death.

2005

Above and Beyond Alaska leads the first hiking tour from the Juneau trail system onto the ice and into the now famous ice caves of the Mendenhall Glacier.

2006

On its June 22 broadcast, *Good Morning America* features the glacier that it ranks 4th of the top 10 outdoor family vacations in the USA.

2014

500,000 visitors per year benchmark is reached.

2014

On July 10, *The Today Show,* broadcasts live from the outdoor pavilion overlooking the glacier. About 1,5 Juneauites show up at 2am at the glacier parking lot for the live broadcast of *The Today Show* scheduled at 3am Alaska time meaning 7am East Coast time.

Page 76-7
Northern lights swirl over th
Mendenhall Glacier. Circa 201

Page 78-7
A ceiling of thick blue ice looms over a hiker in th
underbelly of the Mendenhall Glacier. Circa 20

JUNEAU
ICEFIELD

Herbert
Glacier

Mendenhall
Glacier

Mendenhall
Lake

Lynn Canal

Shelter
Island

Auke Bay

Admiralty
Island

Douglas Island

Downtown
Juneau

Norris Glacier

Taku
Glacier

Gastineau Channel

Taku River

Stephens Passage

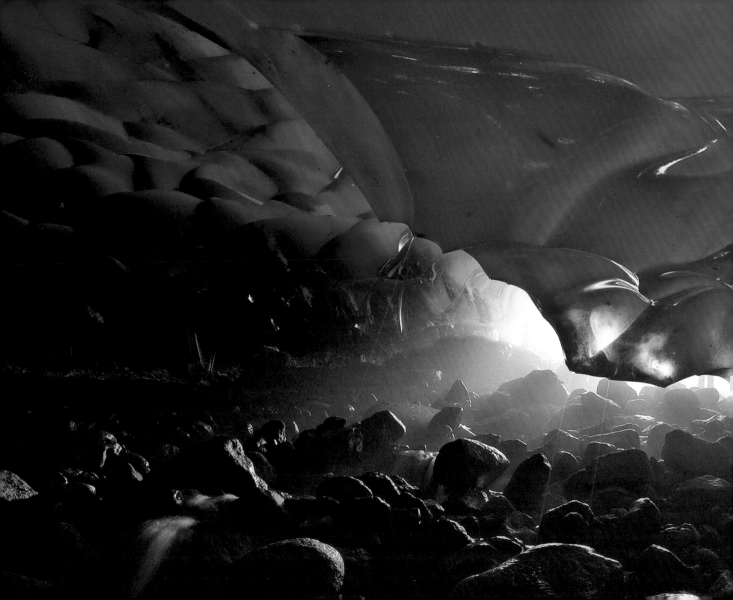

Our Stories

Photo by Charity Green

MARK KELLEY is an award-winning Alaskan photographer. Mark placed Best in Show in the 2017 North American Nature Photography Association Showcase Competition and he won a 2013 Nature's Best Windland Smith Rice Photography Award in the Outdoor Adventure Category. His work in journalism has been recognized by the Alaska Press Club, the National Press Photographers Association, and the Society of Professional Journalists. Mark Kelley's deep roots in photojournalism still influence his work today and he calls himself a "nature photojournalist". His books have sold over a quarter million copies. *Glacier Bay National Park, Alaska, Alaska's Tracy Arm and Sawyer Glaciers,* and *Alaska: A Photographic Excursion* are Benjamin Franklin Award winners; his kid's book *Once Upon Alaska* is a Mom's Choice Awards® Gold recipient. Mark lives in Juneau with his wife, Jan, and their two grown sons also call Juneau home. Mark's late family dog, Rosie, often accompanied Mark on his journeys to the Mendenhall Glacier ice caves.

Photo by Mark Kelley

NICK JANS is one of Alaska's most recognized and prolific writers. A longtime contributing editor to Alaska Magazine and a member of USA Today's board of editorial contributors. He has written twelve books, including the national bestseller, *A Wolf Called Romeo* (Houghton Mifflin, July 2014). Jans is currently working on several book projects, including a long-simmering literary novel set in the Arctic and a collection of Alaska animal essays.

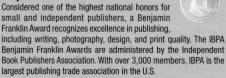

Gold Winner 2018
Benjamin Franklin Award™
Considered one of the highest national honors for small and independent publishers, a Benjamin Franklin Award recognizes excellence in publishing, including writing, photography, design, and print quality. The IBPA Benjamin Franklin Awards are administered by the Independent Book Publishers Association. With over 3,000 members, IBPA is the largest publishing trade association in the U.S.

FRIESENS
IDEAS CRAFTED IN PRINT
EST. 1907

I am proud to print this book with Friesen Corporation in Altona, Manitoba, Canada Friesens is a fully certified FSC printer, a well as a member of the Green Press Initiative The Forest Stewardship Council (FSC) is an international certification and labeling system for products that come from responsibly managed forests and verified recycled sources Friesens uses only hydro-generated power and their inks ar vegetable-based and stored in refillable drums.